Unicorn Activity Book

For Kids

This book belongs to:

_ _ _ _ _ _ _ _ _ _ _ _

_ _ _ _ _ _ _ _ _ _ _ _

UNiCORN
DREAMS

Maze

Help the unicorn reach the moon. You can go under or over the pathways.

Crack the Code

Match each picture to it's letter in the code and write the letter above the picture. Crack the code to find out the message from the unicorns.

Join the Dots

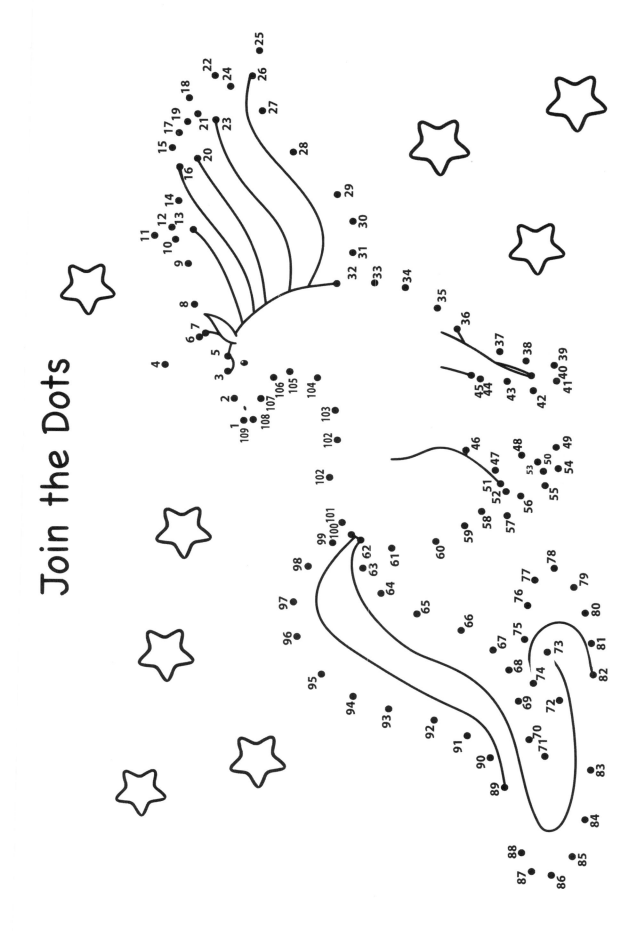

Guess the Unicorn Game

This unicorn:
Has hearts around them.
Has stars in their mane.
Has food.
Is not asleep.

Which unicorn am I?

Play this guessing game with your family or friends. Pick a unicorn and let them guess by asking questions.

Unicorn Word Game (Hangman alternative)

Player 1 picks a word or phrase using the theme below then writes out dashes to show how many letters are in it. Separate each word with a diagonal dash. For example:

— — —/— — —

Player 2 then guesses letters one at a time to figure out what the word or phrase is. Mark off the letters on the alphabet grid as they are guessed. Each time a guessed letter is incorrect, Player 1 should draw a horn onto one of the ponies, to turn them into a unicorn.

Can Player 2 guess the mystery word or phrase before all the ponies turn into unicorns?

The theme of the game is books or television. Write out your dashes below.

a	b	c	d	e	f	g	h	i	j	k	l	m
n	o	p	q	r	s	t	u	v	w	x	y	z

Maze

Help the unicorn reach the rainbow. You can go under and over the pathways. Watch out for the rain cloud!

Spot the Difference

Look close! Can you spot 8 differences?

Tic Tac Toe

Unicorns love Tic Tac Toe. Play it with your family and friends too.
Take it in turns to mark the grid.
Player 1 uses Os. Player 2 uses Xs.
The first to get 3 in a row wins.
The row can be horizontal, vertical or diagonal.

Word 💎 search

```
S  T  A  R  M  B  E  S  I  F  L  Y
S  P  F  E  R  E  Y  E  R  A  O  U
E  N  T  A  A  Y  B  L  R  E  V  B
T  E  V  D  U  T  L  F  E  R  E  F
O  E  R  S  N  P  R  B  N  U  T  S
S  R  E  S  I  L  I  E  N  T  E  Z
M  T  W  N  Q  S  Q  L  U  N  C  S
O  H  S  N  U  I  C  I  R  E  H  M
O  L  T  S  E  P  I  E  W  V  P  A
N  P  R  A  X  S  A  F  C  D  L  W
T  H  O  O  S  A  S  S  F  A  N  I
S  U  N  D  H  O  R  N  N  D  P  N
O  U  G  L  Y  H  G  Y  D  U  C  G
O  X  N  B  A  F  R  I  E  N  D  S
```

Short words:

horn
star
wings
fly
love
sun
moon

Find the words in the puzzle.
Words can be hidden:

Long words:

self belief
brave
resilient
adventure
unique
friends
strong

What's Your Unicorn Name?

Take the first letter of your name and put it together with the month you were born to create your Unicorn Name.

A - Awesome
B - Brilliant
C - Courageous
D - Determined
E - Emerald
F - Fantastic
G - Glitter
H - Happy
I - Ingenius
J - Jubilant
K - Kind
L - Lucky
M - Magnificent

N - Noble
O - Ocean
P - Princess or Prince
Q - Queen or King
R - Royal
S - Strong
T - Twinkly
U - Unique
V - Victorious
W - Wise
X - Exxxceptional
Y - Youthful
Z - Amazzzing

January - Sparkle Soul
February - Heart Healer
March - Rainbow Maker
April - Star Catcher
May - Marvel Mind
June - Flight Taker
July - Dream Creator
August - Heroic Heart
September - Precious Gift
October - Brave One
November - Space Explorer
December - Light Seeker

Let's Count!

How many of each unicorn can you count? Write your answers in the grid below next to each unicorn. For an extra challenge add up the numbers afterwards.

How many unicorns are there in total?

Join the Dots

Now who could this be? Join the dots to find out.
Clue: They are a furry friend of the unicorns.

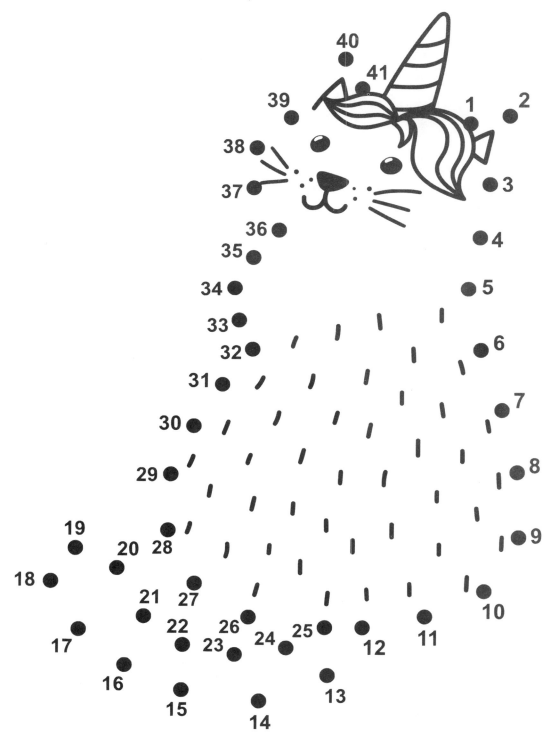

Guess the Unicorn Game

This unicorn is:
Wearing glasses.
Not on a skateboard.
Has a book.
Is wearing a hat.

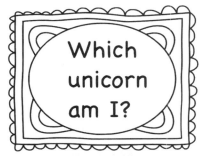
Which unicorn am I?

Play this guessing game with your family and friends. Pick a unicorn and let them guess who it is by asking questions.

Word search

Find the words in the puzzle. Words can be hidden:

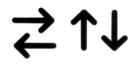

```
U D E B M R S H A R E P
H I C O R S T E H O M E
F A M I L Y B L R E V B
T E Z D T G L A S I E F
L E A R N P A B L U T S
S Y E K I L I M E T E Z
R T W A S H Q L E N C S
I H S N U O C A P S H M
O L T S E U I E W X P S
E P R R X S F K P E A T
A H O O S E F U N A N S
T U J O F U P N N D P E
L U G M W H G Q D U C U
Z D E S A X A L E R D G
```

Short words:
home
live
eat
fun
wash
rooms
sleep

Long words:
family
house
games
guests
learn
share
relax

Spot the Difference

Oh dear unicorn, don't drop that book! Can you spot 7 differences?

Unicorn Word Game (Hangman alternative)

Player 1 picks a word or phrase using the theme below then writes out dashes to show how many letters are in it. Separate each word with a diagonal dash. For example:

__ __ __/__ __ __

Player 2 then guesses letters one at a time to figure out what the word or phrase is. Mark off the letters on the alphabet grid as they are guessed. Each time a guessed letter is incorrect, Player 1 should draw a horn onto one of the ponies, to turn them into a unicorn.

Can Player 2 guess the mystery word or phrase before all the ponies turn into unicorns?

The theme of the game is food and drink. Write out your dashes below.

a	b	c	d	e	f	g	h	i	j	k	l	m
n	o	p	q	r	s	t	u	v	w	x	y	z

Maze

Help the unicorn outside reach the unicorn inside!

Join the Dots

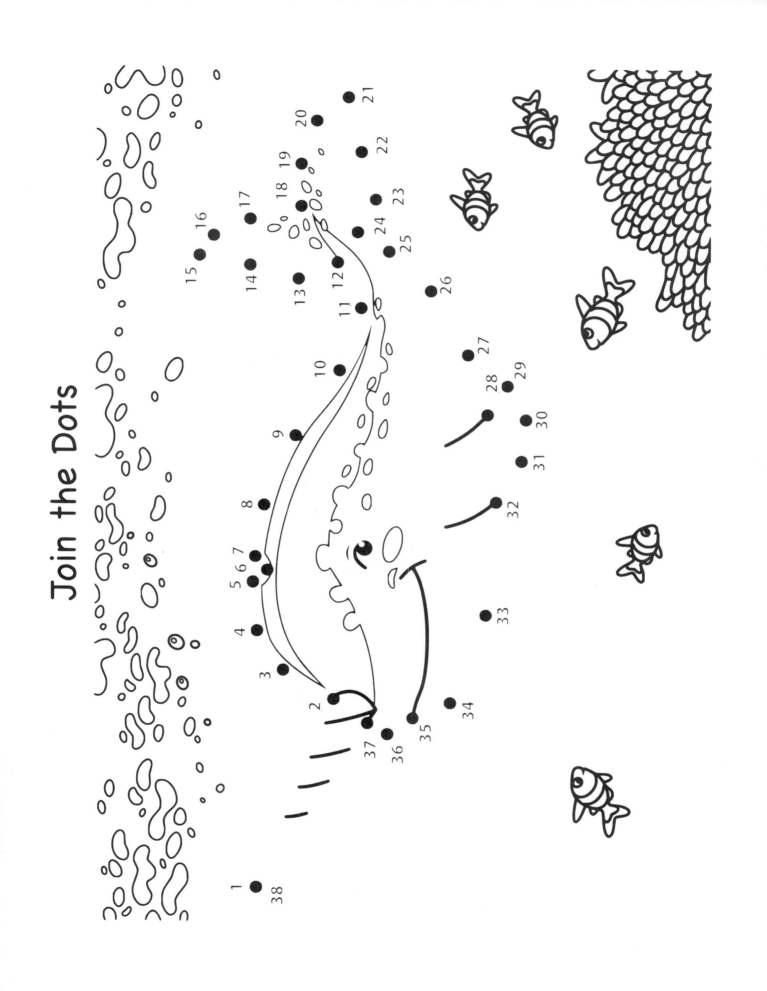

Let's Count!

How many of each sea creature can you count?
Write your answers in the grid below.

Sea Maze

Help the mermaid get home to her friends. You can go under and over the pathways.

Picture Crossword

Solve the 8 numbered picture crossword clues and write them in the
grid to reveal the hidden word running down the centre of the puzzle.

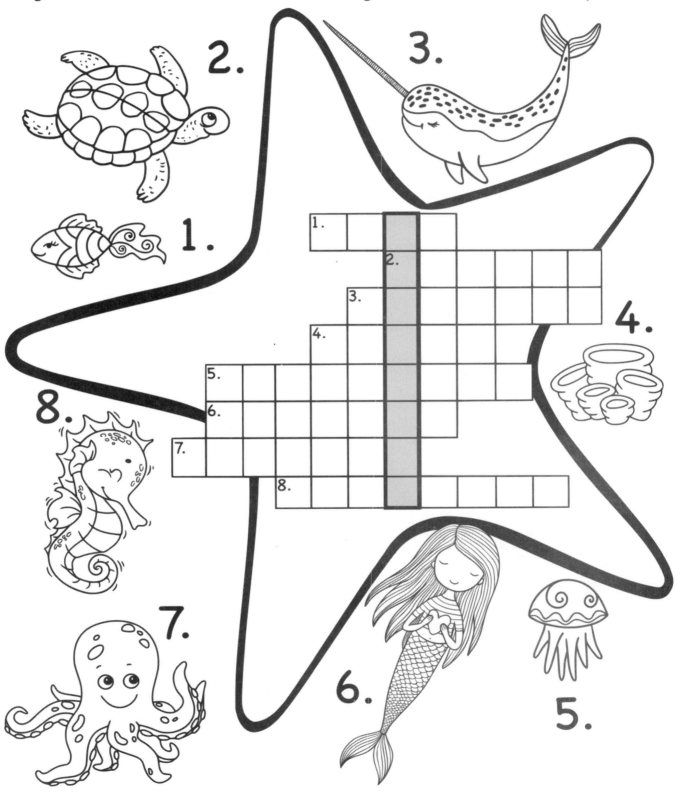

Shadow Matching Game

Draw a line between each Narwhal and their shadow. Can you match all 6?

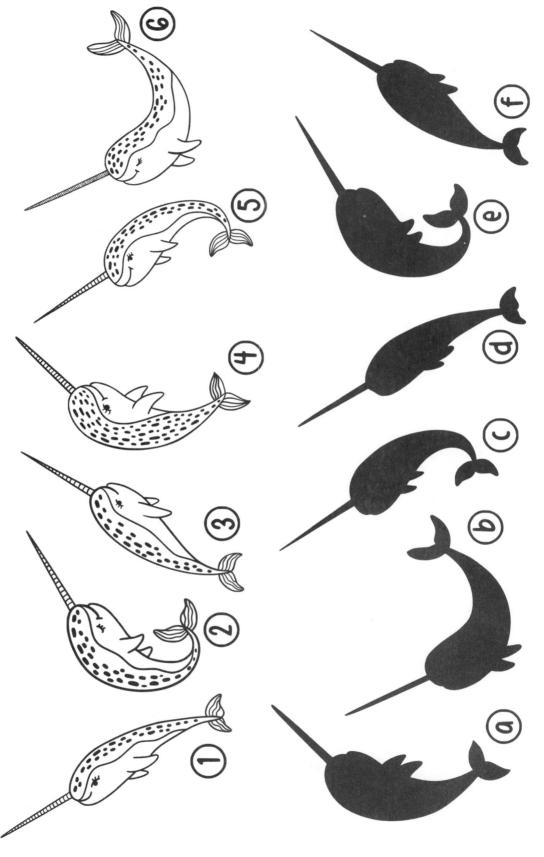

Shell Maze

Help the unicorn reach the mermaid.

Word Search

☆ Are any words new to you? What do they mean? ☆

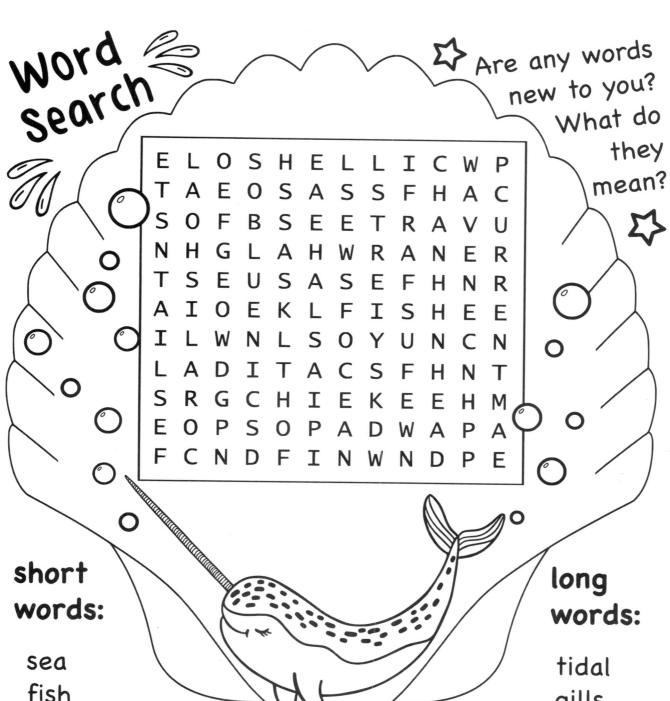

```
E L O S H E L L I C W P
T A E O S A S S F H A C
S O F B S E E T R A V U
N H G L A H W R A N E R
T S E U S A S E F H N R
A I O E K L F I S H E E
I L W N L S O Y U N C N
L A D I T A C S F H N T
S R G C H I E K E E H M
E O P S O P A D W A P A
F C N D F I N W N D P E
```

short words:

sea
fish
shell
fin
wave
tail
blue

Find the words in the puzzle.
Words can be hidden:

⇄ ↑↓ ↘↖ ↙↗

long words:

tidal
gills
coral
shoal
ocean
narwhal
current

Spot the Difference
Can you spot 9 differences?

Unicorn Dreams Activity Answers

Maze
Help the unicorn reach the moon. You can go under or over the pathways.

Crack the code answer - The coded message is: Unicorns dream big!

Join the dots picture:

Unicorn Guessing Game:

This unicorn:
Has hearts around them.
Has stars in their mane.
Has food.
Is not asleep.

Answer:

Maze
Help the unicorn reach the rainbow. You can go under and over the pathways. Watch out for the rain cloud!

Unicorn Dreams Activity Answers

Word search

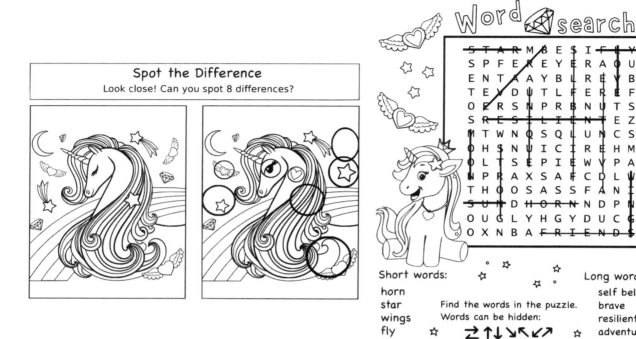

S	T	A	R	M	B	E	S	I	F	L	Y
S	P	F	E	R	E	Y	E	R	A	Q	U
E	N	T	A	A	Y	B	L	R	E	Y	B
T	E	V	D	U	T	L	F	E	R	E	F
O	E	R	S	N	P	R	B	N	U	T	S
S	R	E	S	I	L	I	E	N	T	E	Z
M	T	W	N	Q	S	Q	L	U	N	C	S
O	H	S	N	U	I	C	I	R	E	H	M
O	L	T	S	E	P	I	E	W	C	H	A
N	P	R	A	X	S	A	F	C	D	P	U
T	H	O	O	S	A	S	S	F	A	N	I
S	U	N	D	H	O	R	N	R	L	N	N
O	U	G	L	Y	H	G	Y	D	U	C	G
O	X	N	B	A	F	R	I	E	N	D	S

Short words:
horn
star
wings
fly
love
sun
moon

Find the words in the puzzle.
Words can be hidden:

Long words:
self belief
brave
resilient
adventure
unique
friends
strong

Spot the Difference
Look close! Can you spot 8 differences?

Home Sweet Home Activity Answers

Lets' Count

5	3	4
4	How many unicorns are there in total? **21**	5

Join the dots picture

Home Sweet Home Activity Answers

Guess the Unicorn Game

This unicorn is:
Wearing glasses.
Not on a skateboard.
Has a book.
Is wearing a hat.

Word search

Find the words in the puzzle. Words can be hidden:

```
U D E B M R S H A R E P
H I C O R S T E H O M E
F A M I L Y B L R E V B
T E Z D T G L A S I E F
L E A R N P A B L U T S
S Y E K I L I M E T E Z
R T W A S H Q L E N C S
I H S N U O C A P S H M
O L T S E U I E W X P S
E P R R X S F K P E A T
A H O O S E F U N A N S
T U J O F U P N N D P E
L U G M W H G Q D U C U
Z D E S A X A L E R D G
```

Short words:
home
live
eat
fun
wash
rooms
sleep

Long words:
family
house
games
guests
learn
share
relax

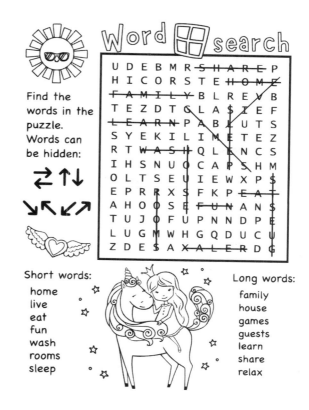

Maze
Help the unicorn outside reach the unicorn inside!

Spot the Difference
Oh dear unicorn, don't drop that book! Can you spot 7 differences?

Sea Magic Activity Answers

Join the Dots:
It's a narwhal!

Let's Count!

9	8	5
7	6	15

Sea Maze

Help the mermaid get home to her friends. You can go under and over the pathways.

Picture Crossword

Solve the 8 numbered picture crossword clues and write them in the grid to reveal the hidden word running down the centre of the puzzle.

1. FISH
2. TURTLE
3. NARWHAL
4. CORAL
5. JELLYFISH
6. MERMAID
7. OCTOPUS
8. SEAHORSE

The hidden word is:

starfish

Sea Magic Activity Answers

Shadow match answers:
1 – d
2 – e
3 – f
4 – a
5 – c
6 – b

Shell Maze
Help the unicorn reach the mermaid.

Word Search

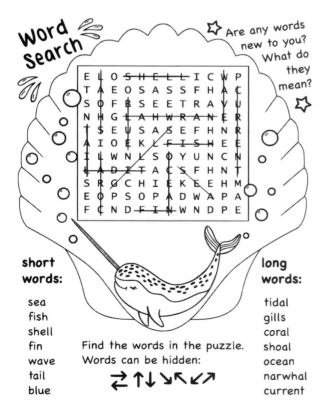

Are any words new to you? What do they mean?

short words:
sea
fish
shell
fin
wave
tail
blue

Find the words in the puzzle.
Words can be hidden:

long words:
tidal
gills
coral
shoal
ocean
narwhal
current

Spot the Difference
Can you spot 9 differences?

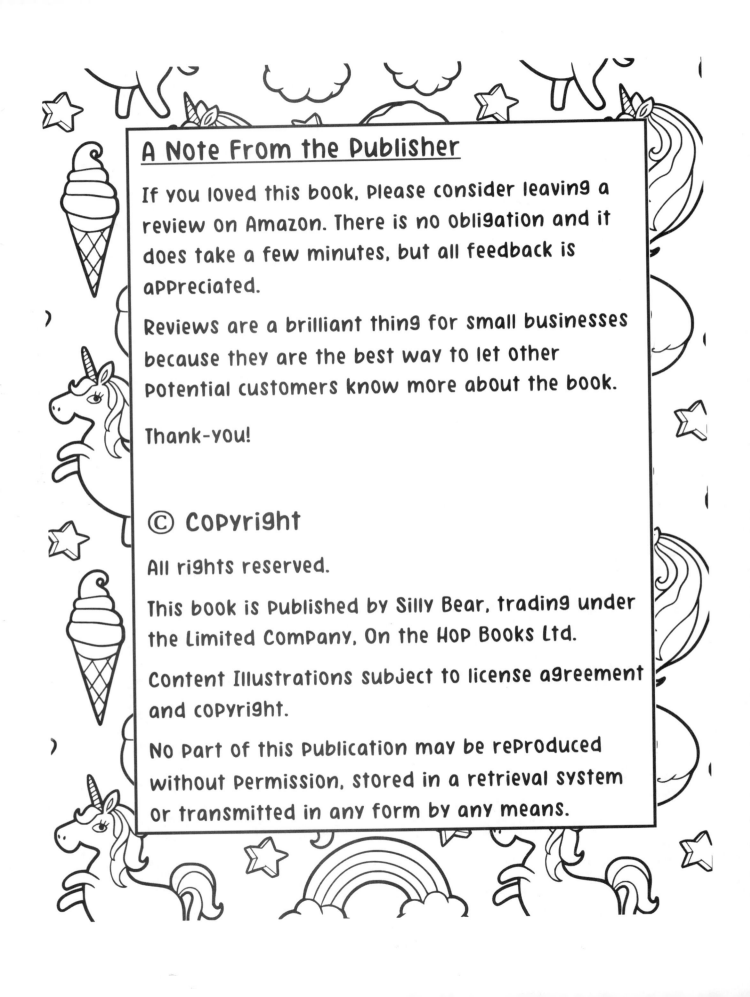

A Note From the Publisher

If you loved this book, please consider leaving a review on Amazon. There is no obligation and it does take a few minutes, but all feedback is appreciated.

Reviews are a brilliant thing for small businesses because they are the best way to let other potential customers know more about the book.

Thank-you!

© Copyright